COLLINS

Student Support Materials for

Edexcel

AS BIOLOGY

Unit 1: Molecules and Cells

Mary Jones
Geoff Jones

This booklet has been designed to support the Edexcel Biology AS. It contains some material which has been added in order to clarify the specification.
The examination will be limited to material set out in the specification document.

Published by HarperCollins*Publishers* Limited
77–85 Fulham Palace Road
Hammersmith
London W6 8JB

www.**Collins**Education.com
Online support for schools and colleges

First published 2000
Reprinted 2001, 2002

ISBN 0 00 327712 7

Mary Jones and Geoff Jones assert the moral right to be identified as authors of this work

British Library Cataloguing in Publication Data
A catalogue record for this publication is available from the British Library

Cover designed by Chi Leung
Editorial, design and production by Gecko Limited, Cambridge
Printed and bound by Scotprint, Haddington

The publisher wishes to thank the Edexcel foundation for permission to reproduce the examination questions.

You might also like to visit
www.**fire**and**water**.com
The book lover's website

Other useful texts for AS

Full colour textbooks
Collins Advanced Science: Biology
Collins Advanced Science: Human Biology

Student Support Booklets
Edexcel Biology: 2 Exchange, Transport and Reproduction
Edexcel Biology: 3 Energy and the Environment

What books do I need to study this course?

You will probably use a range of resources during your course. Some will be produced by the centre where you are studying, some by a commercial publisher and others may be borrowed from libraries or study centres. Different resources have different uses – but remember, owning a book is not enough – it must be *used*.

What does this booklet cover?

This *Student Support Booklet* covers the content you need to know and understand to pass the unit test for Edexcel Biology AS Unit 1: Molecules and Cells. It is very concise and you will need to study it carefully to make sure you can remember all of the material.

How can I remember all this material?

Reading the booklet is an essential first step – but reading by itself is not a good way to get stuff into your memory. If you have bought the booklet and can write on it, you could try the following techniques to help you to memorise the material:

- underline or highlight the most important words in every paragraph
- underline or highlight scientific jargon – write a note of the meaning in the margin if you are unsure
- remember the number of items in a list – then you can tell if you have forgotten one when you try to remember it later
- tick sections when you are sure you know them – and then concentrate on the sections you do not yet know.

How can I check my progress?

The unit test at the end is a useful check on your progress – you may want to wait until you have nearly completed the unit and use it as a mock exam or try questions one by one as you progress. The answers show you how much you need to do to get the marks.

What if I get stuck?

The colour textbook *Collins Advanced Science: Biology* is designed to support your AS course. It provides more explanation than this booklet. It may help you to make progress if you get stuck.

Any other good advice?

- You will not learn well if you are tired or stressed. Set aside time for work (and play!) and try to stick to it.

- Don't leave everything until the last minute – whatever your friends may tell you it doesn't work.

- You are most effective if you work hard for shorter periods of time and then take a (short!) break. 30 minutes of work followed by a five or ten minute break is a useful pattern. Then get back to work.

- Some people work better in the morning, some in the evening. Find out which works better for you and do that whenever possible.

- Do not suffer in silence – ask friends and your teacher for help.

- Stay calm, enjoy it and ... good luck!

The main text gives a very concise explanation of the ideas in your course. You must study all of it – none is spare or not needed.

There are rigorous definitions of the main terms used in your examination – memorise these exactly.

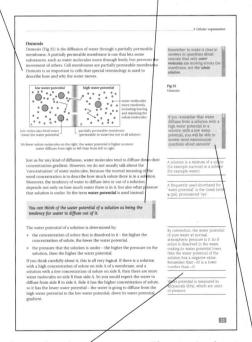

Further explanation references give a little extra detail, or direct you to other texts if you need more help or need to read around a topic.

The examiner's notes are always useful – make sure you read them because they will help with your unit test.

1 Molecules and cells

Living organisms are made up of a wide variety of molecules. The most common atoms found in the molecules that make up living organisms are hydrogen, carbon, oxygen and nitrogen.

Carbon dioxide is inorganic, and so is an exception to the rule that molecules containing carbon are organic.

Substances whose molecules contain carbon atoms, for example carbohydrates, lipids and proteins, are known as **organic** substances. Those that do not contain carbon, such as water, are **inorganic** substances.

Water

Water makes up about 70% of the body mass of most organisms. It is also the environment for aquatic (water-living) organisms. Without liquid water, life could not have evolved on Earth.

Water has the molecular formula H_2O. The molecular formula of a substance tells you what kind of atoms its molecules contain, and how many of each. So the formula of water tells you that its molecules each contain two hydrogen atoms and one oxygen atom.

In a water molecule, the two hydrogen atoms are held to the oxygen atom because they share electrons with each other (Fig 1). However, the oxygen atom gets slightly more than its fair share of the electrons. Electrons have a negative charge, and so the oxygen atom has a slight negative charge. The hydrogen atoms have a slight positive charge. The molecule is said to be **dipolar**.

Fig 1
A water molecule

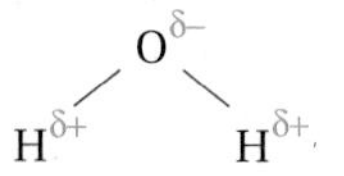

$$O^{\delta-}$$

$$H^{\delta+} \qquad H^{\delta+}$$

Key
$\delta+$ small positive charge
$\delta-$ small negative charge
— single covalent bond
      involving the sharing of
      two electrons

In a liquid, molecules move about constantly, bumping into each other and then moving apart again. In water, the negative parts of the molecules are attracted to the positive parts of other molecules.

Fig 2
Hydrogen bonding
between water molecules

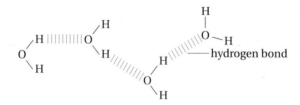
hydrogen bond

These attractive forces, shown in Fig 2, are called **hydrogen bonds**. They tend to hold the water molecules more closely together than is the case in most other kinds of liquids. This results in water having several unusual properties that are of great importance to living organisms. These include:

Hydrogen bonds are also important in the structure of carbohydrates and proteins, where they help to hold a molecule in a particular shape, or help to hold two or more molecules together.

- high specific heat capacity

- high latent heat of vaporisation

- high surface tension
- relatively high density
- excellent solvent properties.

Specific heat capacity

When a liquid is heated, the molecules move about faster and faster. The temperature of a substance is related to the kinetic energy (movement energy) of its molecules. The faster the molecules are moving about, the higher the temperature. The amount of energy required to increase the temperature of 1 g of a substance by 1 °C is called its **specific heat capacity.**

Water has a very high specific heat capacity. This is because water molecules are attracted to each other, so it takes a great deal of energy to make them move about a lot. You have to put a lot of energy into a container of liquid water to make its temperature rise by very much.

This is useful to living organisms. Aquatic organisms live in a liquid whose temperature does not change rapidly, no matter whether it is a hot or cold day. They have a stable environment.

Because all organisms contain a lot of water, their cells are protected from rapid temperature changes. The water in their bodies can absorb or lose a lot of energy without changing temperature by very much. This helps organisms to regulate their body temperature.

Whereas terrestrial (land-living) organisms in Britain may have to cope with temperature fluctuations of between −10 °C and 30 °C during the year, an aquatic organism living in the sea or in a large lake probably only experiences temperatures ranging between 7 °C and 16 °C.

Latent heat of vaporisation

The amount of heat energy required to turn a given quantity of a liquid into a gas is called its **latent heat of vaporisation**. For water, this is high, because the attractions between the water molecules hold them together and make it difficult for them to escape as a gas. This explains why water is mostly in liquid form, and not a gas, on Earth.

Water's high latent heat of vaporisation helps mammals to cool down. They secrete a watery fluid, sweat, onto the surface of their skin. The water in the sweat absorbs heat from the skin as it turns to water vapour. Plant leaves are cooled in a similar way, as water evaporates from the mesophyll cells inside the leaf.

Surface tension

The attractions between water molecules pull the ones on the top of a body of liquid downwards towards all the others. This makes the top of the water behave as though it has a 'skin'. Small animals such as pond skaters can walk on this surface.

Density

Water has a relatively high density compared with other liquids such as ethanol. This is because the hydrogen bonding between the molecules pulls them close together. Most living organisms have a density that is very similar to that of water, and so they tend to float in it. This makes it relatively easy for aquatic organisms to swim in water.

Solvent properties

Many substances can dissolve in water. Molecules that have dipoles are attracted to the charges on the water molecules, so they spread out easily amongst them. Many small organic molecules, such as glucose and amino acids, are soluble in water. Ions, such as Na^+ and Cl^-, also dissolve in water (Fig 3).

Fig 3
How substances dissolve in water

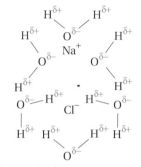

In solid sodium chloride, the sodium and chloride ions are held firmly together in a regular pattern by ionic bonds.

Sodium and chloride ions in solution are kept apart from each other because water molecules are attracted to them and surround them.

Key
- - - - ionic bond attraction between
   positive and negative ions
Na^+ sodium ion
Cl^- chloride ion

Water is also a reactant in many metabolic reactions. For example, it is involved in hydrolysis reactions such as the breakdown of disaccharides to monosaccharides. It is also an important reactant in photosynthesis.

Most globular proteins, such as haemoglobin, can dissolve in water even though their molecules are very large.

Watery liquids, such as blood in animals or phloem sap in plants, transport substances in solution from one part of the organism to another. Metabolic reactions (the chemical reactions that happen inside living organisms) take place in solution, because in this state the reactants are free to move around and react with each other.

Some substances with very large molecules, such as starch or the protein keratin, are insoluble in water. So are those whose molecules carry no overall charge or dipoles, such as lipids. These kinds of substances can form structures, such as cell membranes or hair, that do not dissolve in water. They can also be useful as insoluble storage compounds, such as starch granules in plant cells.

Carbohydrates 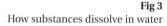 C H O

Carbohydrates are organic substances whose molecules contain carbon, hydrogen and oxygen, where the ratio of carbon, hydrogen and oxygen is approximately 1C : 2H : 1O. They contain —OH groups.

Carbohydrates with *small* molecules are called sugars. All sugars dissolve in water, and taste sweet. Carbohydrates with *large* molecules are called polysaccharides, and include cellulose and starches. They are insoluble in water and do not taste sweet.

Monosaccharides

A monosaccharide is a carbohydrate whose molecules are a single sugar unit. The general formula for a monosaccharide is $C_nH_{2n}O_n$. Monosaccharides that contain five carbon atoms are called pentoses. Their molecular formula is usually $C_5H_{10}O_5$. Two important pentoses are shown in Fig 4.

Fig 4
Ribose and
deoxyribose

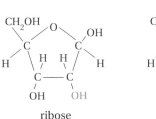

ribose   deoxyribose

Monosaccharides that contain six carbon atoms are called **hexoses**. Their molecular formula is $C_6H_{12}O_6$. These atoms can be arranged in different ways, forming different hexoses.

The hexose monosaccharide **glucose** can exist in the α or β form (Fig 5). This does not make any difference to its properties, but it does greatly affect the properties of molecules made when the glucose molecules link together.

hat, in Figs 4 and 5 all
ns in the molecules are
whereas in Fig 6 the
in the rings are missed
out. In Fig 7 most of the Hs and
OHs are missed out as well. All
of these are acceptable ways of
representing molecules, but if
you are asked to draw a
monosaccharide or a
disaccharide molecule in an
examination answer, you
should show *all* of the atoms
to be sure of getting full marks.

Fig 5
α and β glucose
molecules

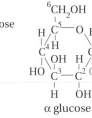

α glucose

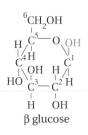

β glucose

Table 1
Some important monosaccharides

Monosaccharide	Hexose or pentose?	Roles
glucose	hexose	• the main substrate for respiration • the form in which carbohydrate is transported in mammalian blood • the building block (monomer) for many other carbohydrates, such as starch and cellulose
fructose	hexose	• found in nectar and many fruits; it is sweeter than glucose, and helps to attract animals for pollination and fruit dispersal • with glucose, forms the disaccharide sucrose
galactose	hexose	• with glucose, forms the disaccharide lactose
ribose	pentose	• a component of RNA
deoxyribose	pentose	• a component of DNA

Disaccharides

Monosaccharides can link together to form larger molecules. Carbohydrates whose molecules contain two monosaccharides (sugar units) linked together are called **disaccharides**. Disaccharides are sugars and so are sweet and soluble.

Different pairs of monosaccharides can link together to make different disaccharides. For example, two glucose molecules can link together to form the disaccharide **maltose** (Fig 6).

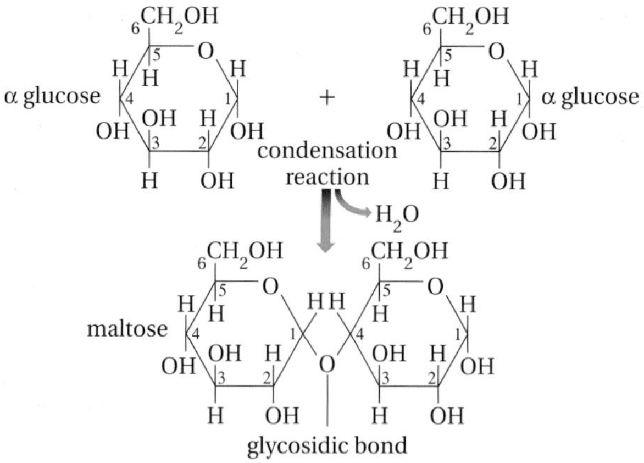

Fig 6
A condensation reaction between two glucose molecules forms a maltose molecule

> **D**
>
> *A reaction in which two molecules are joined together with the elimination of a molecule of water is called a* **condensation reaction**. *The bond joining two glucose molecules is called a* **glycosidic bond**.

The hydrolysis of maltose to glucose takes place during digestion, in the small intestine.

The maltose molecule can be broken apart to form two separate glucose molecules. This reaction requires a water molecule to be added, and so it is called an **hydrolysis reaction**.

Table 2
Some important disaccharides

Condensation and hydrolysis reactions are also involved in the build-up and breakdown of other important molecules in living organisms, such as proteins and nucleic acids.

N.B. disaccharides & polysaccharides are composed of MONOMERS joined by GLYCOSIDIC BONDS.

Disaccharide	Monosaccharide units (monomers)	Roles
maltose	glucose + glucose	• formed from the breakdown of starch in germinating seeds, where it provides energy to the growing embryo
sucrose	glucose + fructose	• the form in which carbohydrates are transported in the phloem of plants
lactose	glucose + galactose	• an energy source for young mammals, in milk

Polysaccharides

Polysaccharides are carbohydrates whose molecules are **polymers** – that is, they are made from many monosaccharide monomers linked together. They are very large molecules, and so are not soluble in water. They do not taste sweet.

You can buy 'soluble starch', which is made of starch whose molecules have been broken down into shorter lengths of glucose molecules.

Starch (Fig 7) is actually a mixture of two polysaccharides, **amylose** and **amylopectin**. Amylose is made of many α glucose units, linked with glycosidic bonds between carbon 1 on one glucose and carbon 4 on the next. A shorthand way of writing this is to say that they are $\alpha(1-4)$ links. Amylopectin is also formed of $\alpha(1-4)$ linked glucose, but has branches where the linkages are $\alpha(1-6)$.

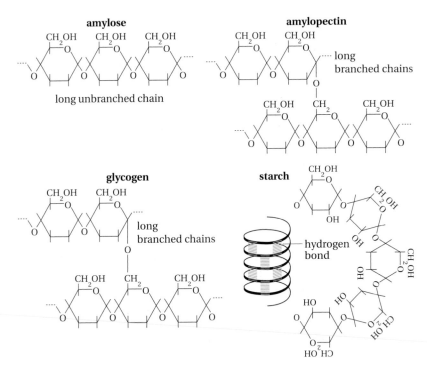

Fig 7
The structure of starch and glycogen

The long chains of glucose joined by $\alpha(1-4)$ bonds form spirals held by hydrogen bonding in all these molecules (except at $\alpha(1-6)$ branches)

Starch molecules curl up into spirals. They are held in this shape by hydrogen bonds between the —OH groups of different glucose units. Starch is the main storage carbohydrate in plant cells, where it forms grains inside chloroplasts. It is very compact and, because it is insoluble, it does not affect the water potential of the cell. It can easily be broken down by the enzyme amylase, providing maltose and glucose as soluble energy sources.

Water potential is explained on page 33.

Glycogen has a similar structure to amylopectin. It is the storage carbohydrate of animals, and is found in liver and muscle cells.

$\alpha(1-4) + \alpha(1-6)$ glycosidic bonds
↑
more than amylopectin

Cellulose (Fig 8) is a polymer of β glucose, joined with (1–4) links. Its molecules do not curl up, but form long straight chains. These chains tend to lie parallel to each other, forming a bundle of molecules called a **microfibril**, held together by hydrogen bonds between adjacent chains. These microfibrils have great tensile strength, and are an important structural component of plant cell walls. They are insoluble, and difficult to digest, because few organisms make an enzyme that can break the $\beta(1-4)$ linkages.

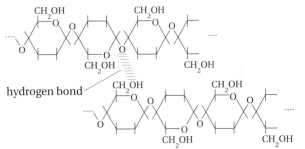

Fig 8
The structure of cellulose

Glucose molecules joined by $\beta(1-4)$ bonds form long, straight cellulose molecules. Adjacent cellulose molecules are hydrogen bonded.

Lipids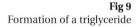

Lipids include fats, oils and waxes. Their molecules contain carbon, hydrogen and oxygen, but with a far smaller proportion of oxygen than in carbohydrates. Lipids are insoluble in water.

Fig 9 shows the structure of a **triglyceride**, that is a lipid formed from glycerol and three fatty acids, linked by **ester bonds**. Fatty acids contain carboxyl groups, —COOH. The fatty acids may be **saturated** or **unsaturated**. In a saturated fatty acid, every carbon atom in the chain has two hydrogens bonded to it. In an unsaturated fatty acid, two or more of the carbons have only one hydrogen attached, and the bonds that could have linked to more hydrogen atoms link to the next-door carbon instead, forming a double bond. Triglycerides which contain unsaturated fatty acids tend to be liquid at room temperature, and are called **oils**. Those which contain saturated fatty acids tend to be solid at room temperature, and are called **fats** and **waxes**.

Fig 9
Formation of a triglyceride

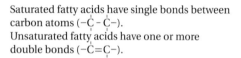

glycerol

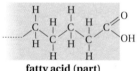

fatty acid (part)

Saturated fatty acids have single bonds between carbon atoms (−C̶ - C̶−).
Unsaturated fatty acids have one or more double bonds (−C̶=C̶−).

An ester bond formed by a condensation reaction between – OH and – COOH

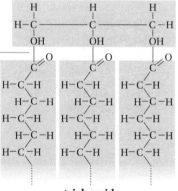

triglyceride

The roles of triglycerides include:

- energy storage
- buoyancy
- protection
- waterproofing
- thermal insulation.

Triglycerides are useful energy stores in animals and plants, because they are insoluble in water and can be stored as droplets inside cells. They have a relatively low density and contain about twice as much energy per gram as polysaccharides. Many aquatic mammals, such as whales, have cells which contain large amounts of fat beneath their skin. These cells make up **adipose tissue**, which not only serves as an energy store, but also provides the animal with buoyancy, and insulates it against heat loss from its body into the water. Humans, too, have adipose tissue beneath the skin, and also around some of the internal organs such as the kidneys, where it provides a cushioning layer to protect against mechanical damage. Waxes and oils make excellent waterproofing layers, such as the oils on the feathers of ducks, and the waxy cuticle on the leaves of plants.

Phospholipids (Fig 10) are lipids formed from glycerol, two fatty acids and a phosphate group. The fatty acid part of the molecule is not attracted to water, and is said to be **hydrophobic**. However, the phosphate part is soluble in water, and is said to be **hydrophilic**. So, in water, phospholipids tend to arrange themselves in a double layer, with the phosphate 'heads' in the water, and the fatty acid 'tails' away from it. This phospholipid bilayer is the basic structure that forms all cell membranes.

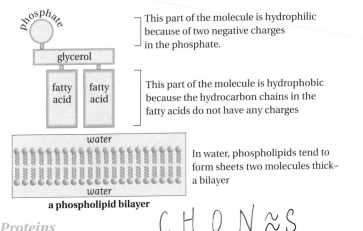

This part of the molecule is hydrophilic because of two negative charges in the phosphate.

This part of the molecule is hydrophobic because the hydrocarbon chains in the fatty acids do not have any charges

In water, phospholipids tend to form sheets two molecules thick– a bilayer

a phospholipid bilayer

Fig 10
Phospholipids

Proteins

$C \ H \ O \ N \approx S$

Proteins are polymers made of monomers called **amino acids**. All amino acids contain carbon, hydrogen, oxygen and nitrogen atoms, and some of them also contain sulphur. An amino acid molecule contains an **amino group**, $-NH_2$, and a **carboxyl group**, $-COOH$ (Fig 11). There are about 20 different naturally occurring amino acids, which differ from each other in their R groups. The general formula for an amino acid is $NH_2.RCH.COOH$.

NB AMINO ACIDS ARE MONOMERS, FORMING PROTEINS AND POLYPEPTIDES.

Fig 11
Amino acids

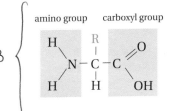

NB

amino group   carboxyl group

The simplest amino acid is glycine, in which R is a hydrogen atom. The other 19 amino acids all have more complex R groups, always containing carbon and hydrogen, and sometimes nitrogen, oxygen and sulphur

Two amino acids can join together in a condensation reaction to form a **dipeptide**, in which the two monomers are linked by a **peptide bond** (Fig 12). Dipeptides can be broken down into their individual amino acids by hydrolysis reactions.

Fig 12
How amino acids link together

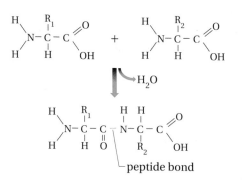

A chain formed of many amino acids linked in this way is called a **polypeptide**. There is no clear difference between a polypeptide and a protein, but in general the term 'protein' is used either for a very large polypeptide molecule, or for a molecule that is made up of several polypeptide molecules held together.

The amino acids are linked together to form polypeptide molecules on the ribosomes of cells. The sequence in which the amino acids are linked is determined by the code stored in the DNA molecules in the nucleus.

Ribosomes are described on page 28.

A polypeptide molecule can contain any number of the 20 different amino acids, in any proportions, and linked together in any order. Different sequences of amino acids form different polypeptides. The sequence of amino acids in a polypeptide molecule is called its **primary structure**. There is an infinite number of possible primary structures, and therefore an infinite number of polypeptides that can be made.

Polypeptide molecules often curl or fold into regular 3-D shapes that are known as the **secondary structure**. This may be an α helix or a β strand. There may be further folding, called the **tertiary structure**, in which the already-folded molecule curls into a complex 3-D shape. Sometimes, a polypeptide may associate with other polypeptides, or with a non-protein component, to form a protein with **quaternary structure** (Fig 13).

Fig 13
Protein structure

Note: Amino acids can be identified by three letters, usually the first three letters of their name, e.g. Phe is the amino acid phenylalanine.

Primary structure: Amino acid sequence

part of the primary structure of a protein

Secondary structure: First level of 3-D shape

α helix   β strand

← RESULTING FROM HYDROGEN BONDING

Note: In this diagram a cylinder represents an α helix.

Tertiary structure: Second level of 3-D shape

← FOLDING OF SECONDARY STRUCTURE
← 3D SHAPE
← MAINTAINED BY H-BONDS, IONIC, DISULPHIDE BONDS
← BONDING DETERMINED BY R-GROUPS
← SHAPE IMPORTANT FOR FUNCTION

Quaternary structure: Arrangement of polypeptides, if more than one is present

Note: In this diagram each polypeptide is shown as a single 'blob'.

four polypeptides

Each type of polypeptide or protein folds into a very precise shape that is determined by its primary structure. The molecule is held in this shape by bonds that form between different amino acids in the chain. These bonds are:

- **ionic bonds**, which form between R groups containing $-NH_3^+$ and those containing $-COO^-$
- **hydrogen bonds**, which form between groups with dipoles
- **disulphide bonds**, which form between the sulphur-containing R groups of the amino acid cysteine.

Insulin

Insulin (Fig 14) is a protein with a quaternary structure, made of two polypeptide chains that are held together by disulphide bonds. Each polypeptide chain contains areas whose secondary structure is an α helix, and one of the chains also has an area where the secondary structure is a β strand. The tertiary structure of each polypeptide chain is held in shape by hydrogen bonds and ionic bonds.

The whole molecule forms an approximately spherical shape, and so insulin is a **globular** protein. Like most globular proteins, it is soluble in water.

Insulin is a hormone that is made in the pancreas and acts on the liver cells. As it is soluble, it can be transported in solution in blood plasma. A particular area on the surface of the insulin molecule can form temporary bonds with insulin receptor molecules in the plasma membranes of liver cells.

Many globular proteins have R groups that carry charges on the outer surfaces of their molecules. This helps them to dissolve in water.

Fig 14
Insulin

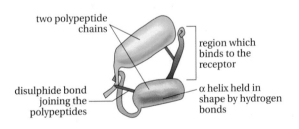

two polypeptide chains

region which binds to the receptor

disulphide bond joining the polypeptides

α helix held in shape by hydrogen bonds

Collagen

Collagen (Fig 15), unlike insulin, is an insoluble protein. This results from the fact that its molecules do not curl up into a ball, but form long chains. So collagen is a **fibrous** protein. Each collagen molecule is formed from three helical polypeptides that wind around each other to form a three-stranded 'rope', held together by hydrogen bonds. Many of these molecules lie side by side, held together by bonds between the $-COOH$ group at the end of some polypeptide molecules and the $-NH_2$ groups at the ends of others. This makes a really strong structure called a collagen **fibril**.

Collagen fibrils are found in skin, bones, tendons, teeth, and the walls of blood vessels. Collagen is an important structural material, conferring strength and elasticity. This is because the twisted, rope-like structure can be pulled out a little straighter, but naturally recoils when released.

Fig 15
Collagen

secondary structure of collagen – a helix unique to collagen, stabilised by hydrogen bonds

tertiary structure – the collagen helix is wound into a loose spiral

quaternary structure – three polypeptide chains form a triple helix stabilised by hydrogen bonds between the chains

Nucleic acids

E When you first mention one of the bases in an examination answer, it is a good idea to write the name in full. After that, you can use the one-letter abbreviation. Take care to spell them correctly! Do not confuse thymine with thiamine, or adenine with adenosine.

Nucleic acids are polymers composed of monomers called **nucleotides** (Fig 16). A nucleotide is a molecule composed of an organic **base**, a **pentose sugar** and a **phosphate** group.

The bases have molecules shaped in a ring, containing nitrogen. A **pyrimidine** base has one ring, and a **purine** has two. There are five bases: **adenine**, **thymine**, **guanine**, **cytosine** and **uracil**. They are often written as the abbreviations **A**, **T**, **G**, **C** and **U**. A and G are purines, and T, C and U are pyrimidines.

The pentose sugar can be either **ribose** or **deoxyribose**. A nucleotide containing ribose is a ribonucleotide, while one containing deoxyribose is a deoxyribonucleotide.

Nucleotides can join together by condensation reactions to form polymers called **polynucleotides**. These can be **ribonucleic acid**, **RNA**, if the monomers contain ribose, or **deoxyribonucleic acid**, **DNA**, if they contain deoxyribose.

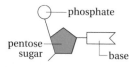

pentose—
sugar
phosphate
base

Fig 16
A nucleotide

The structure of DNA and RNA

A DNA molecule is made of two polynucleotide strands, running in opposite directions, wound around each other to form a double helix. Each strand has a backbone of alternating deoxyribose and phosphate groups, with the bases projecting into the centre of the helix. The bases are held together by hydrogen bonds (Fig 17). Purine bases always pair with pyrimidines. **A** always pairs with **T**, while **C** always pairs with **G**. This is known as **complementary base pairing**. There are two hydrogen bonds between A and T, and three between C and G.

purine	hydrogen bonds	pyrimidine
A	------------------------	T
G	------------------------	C

The structure of RNA is just like that of DNA, except that:

- an RNA molecule has only one polynucleotide strand, not two
- RNA contains ribose, not deoxyribose
- RNA contains the base uracil, whereas DNA contains thymine.

DNA replication

DNA molecules are able to copy themselves exactly, in a process known as **semi-conservative replication**, shown in Fig 18. It is called semi-conservative because half (semi) of the original molecule is kept (conserved) in the new molecule that is made. DNA replication is controlled by a number of enzymes, including DNA polymerase. The steps in replication are:

1 The double helix unwinds, and the two strands separate as the hydrogen bonds between the bases break.

2 Free nucleotides that are present in the cell pair up with the exposed complementary base on each strand. Hydrogen bonds form between the bases.

3 The phosphate group of one nucleotide forms a bond with the deoxyribose group of the one lying next to it, to form a new strand.

Fig 17
The structure of DNA

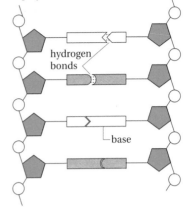

one polynucleotide

hydrogen bonds

base

DNA polymerase enzyme moves along the DNA molecule, 'unzips' it and catalyses the joining of nucleotides

Fig 18
How DNA replicates

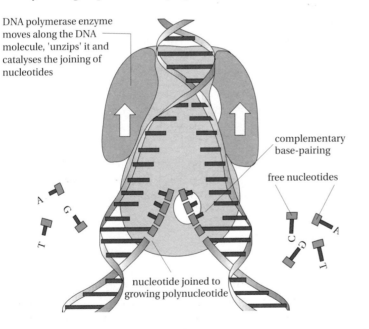

complementary base-pairing

free nucleotides

nucleotide joined to growing polynucleotide

DNA replication takes place in the nucleus, during **interphase** of the cell cycle. Very few mistakes are made in copying the base sequence exactly, because DNA polymerase will only link a nucleotide into the growing chain if the bases are paired correctly.

How DNA codes for protein synthesis

The DNA molecules in a cell determine the polypeptides and proteins made by that cell. Proteins are made by linking together amino acids in a particular sequence, on the ribosomes in the cytoplasm of a cell. The sequence of bases in a DNA molecule in the nucleus determines the sequence of amino acids in the protein that is made in the cytoplasm. A length of DNA that contains the instructions for making one polypeptide is called a **gene**.

When you are describing DNA replication, remember that the nucleotides are there already in the cell, and all that has to be done is to link them together in the right order. It is not correct to say that the nucleotides are 'made' during this process.

The way in which the base sequence is translated into an amino acid sequence depends upon the **genetic code**. In this code, which is almost the same in every organism, three bases in a DNA molecule code for one amino acid. A sequence of three bases in a DNA molecule is called an **anticodon**. There are 64 possible anticodons, and only 20 different amino acids, so some amino acids have two or more different anticodons that represent them. For example, the base sequences CCA, CCG, CCT and CCC all mean 'place a glycine molecule here in the protein'. Other anticodons represent 'start here' or 'stop here'.

Protein synthesis has two stages: **transcription** and **translation**. In transcription (Fig 19):

1 The part of the DNA molecule that contains the code for making a particular protein unwinds, and the two strands separate, exposing the bases.

2 Free RNA nucleotides that are already in the nucleus slot into place against their complementary bases on one of the DNA strands.

3 The phosphate and ribose groups of the RNA nucleotides are linked together by the enzyme RNA polymerase, forming a **messenger RNA molecule (mRNA)**.

4 The mRNA molecule breaks away from the DNA, and moves out of the nucleus into the cytoplasm.

Fig 19
Transcription

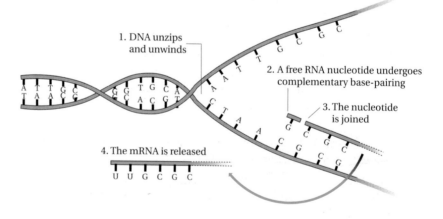

1. DNA unzips and unwinds

2. A free RNA nucleotide undergoes complementary base-pairing

3. The nucleotide is joined

4. The mRNA is released

Remember that RNA contains uracil instead of thymine, so the complementary base for adenine will be uracil.

Notice that the mRNA strand forms against just *one* of the DNA strands. This DNA strand is sometimes called the 'sense' strand.

So, the mRNA molecule now contains a complementary copy of the base sequence on the DNA molecule. If the sequence of bases on the DNA molecule was

ATA CCG GCA TTT TAC

then the sequence of bases on the mRNA molecule will be

UAU GGC CGU AAA AUG

The base triplets on the mRNA molecule are called **codons**.

The mRNA lies against a ribosome in the cytoplasm of the cell, where the protein will be synthesised. The second stage of the process, translation, takes place as shown in Fig 20.

Fig 20
Translation

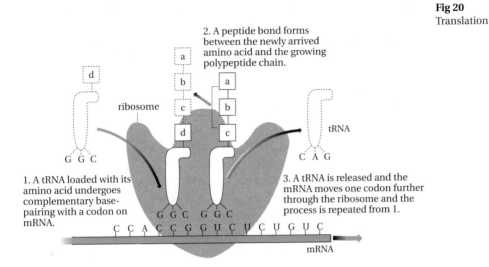

2. A peptide bond forms between the newly arrived amino acid and the growing polypeptide chain.

ribosome

tRNA

1. A tRNA loaded with its amino acid undergoes complementary base-pairing with a codon on mRNA.

3. A tRNA is released and the mRNA moves one codon further through the ribosome and the process is repeated from 1.

mRNA

Already present in the cytoplasm are all the different types of amino acids, and also many different RNA molecules of another type, called **transfer RNA (tRNA)**. Each tRNA molecule has a sequence of three bases – an anticodon – at one end. At the other end of each tRNA, an amino acid can bond. The particular amino acid a tRNA molecule will link up with is determined by its anticodon. Thus, a tRNA molecule with the base sequence CCA carries a glycine molecule.

1 The mRNA molecule is held by the ribosome with two codons (six bases) in a position that tRNA molecules can bind with.

2 A tRNA molecule with the complementary anticodon to the mRNA's first codon binds to the mRNA, as hydrogen bonds form between the complementary bases. A second tRNA binds in a similar way to the mRNA's second codon.

3 The amino acids that the two adjacent tRNAs are carrying are joined together by the formation of a peptide bond.

4 The first tRNA molecule leaves the ribosome. A third tRNA, complementary to the third mRNA codon, brings its amino acid and adds it to the growing chain.

5 The process continues until a 'stop' codon is reached on the mRNA. The peptide chain then leaves the ribosome.

The Human Genome Project
In 1990, an international project was begun to attempt to find the base sequences of all the DNA in the nucleus of a human cell. This is called the **Human Genome Project** – the word 'genome' means all the genes that are present in an organism. The hope is that, if we know more about the DNA make-up of humans, we may be able to understand more about how our genes affect the behaviour of cells. From this, we may be able to develop

Remember that the base triplets are called anticodons on DNA and tRNA, and codons on mRNA.

The fact that a tRNA molecule with a particular anticodon binds with a particular amino acid is crucial to the functioning of the genetic code.

E It is easy to get so bogged down with the details of transcription and translation that you lose the 'big picture' – which is that the sequence of *bases* on the DNA molecule is used to determine the sequence of *amino acids* in a polypeptide chain.

E You may be asked to describe the particular roles of mRNA or tRNA, so make sure that you understand just how they contribute to the overall process.

E You should be prepared to discuss the social and ethical issues associated with the Human Genome Project. Try to base your arguments on scientific fact as far as possible.

better treatments for diseases that are caused by 'faulty' alleles of certain genes. Cystic fibrosis is such a disease. Finding the *gene* that is responsible for this disease and working out its base sequence could help in several ways:

- Knowing the base sequence of the faulty allele can help us to understand the structure of the faulty *protein* that it codes for. This might make it easier to develop drugs to treat the disease.

- It may eventually become possible to replace a faulty allele with a correct one, in a process called **gene therapy**. However, so far most attempts at gene therapy have not been very successful, and many more years of research will be needed before this becomes possible.

- A person who knows that a member of their family has a disease caused by a faulty allele might want to know if they, too, have this allele in their cells. If the base sequence of the allele is known, then it becomes possible to test for its presence.

However, it is possible that this kind of information could be used in ways that not everyone would be comfortable with. For example, health insurance companies might ask potential customers to have a DNA analysis done before they will accept them. It is also conceivable that parents might want to have embryos tested for particular alleles before deciding whether or not to allow the baby to develop and be born.

Biochemical tests

Table 3
Biochemical tests

All monosaccharides and most disaccharides are reducing sugars. Sucrose is a non-reducing sugar.

Substance tested for	How test is carried out	Positive result
starch	add iodine in potassium iodide solution	blue-black colour
reducing sugar	add Benedict's solution, bring to boiling point then stop heating	yellow, orange or brick-red precipitate
non-reducing sugar	test for reducing sugar; if negative, take a fresh sample and boil with hydrochloric acid (to hydrolyse to reducing sugar), then add weak alkali to neutralise before testing for reducing sugar again	yellow, orange or brick-red precipitate
protein	add biuret reagent (dilute copper(II) sulphate solution and potassium hydroxide solution)	violet colour

All of these tests can be made **quantitative** by comparing the intensity of the colour you obtain with the unknown substance to the colour obtained with a substance whose concentration you know. You can just do this by eye for an approximate estimation. For more precise measurements, a colorimeter is used.

2 Enzymes

Most metabolic reactions that take place within a living organism would not happen unless catalysed by an enzyme. Enzymes can work both inside and outside cells.

As enzymes are catalysts, they are not altered by the reaction that they catalyse. In an enzyme-catalysed reaction, the substance that is present at the beginning of the reaction is called the **substrate** and the new substance that is formed is the **product.**

substrate $\xrightarrow{\text{enzyme}}$ product

Enzyme structure

Enzymes are globular proteins. Most of them are soluble, though some remain permanently fixed within cell membranes. The tertiary structure of an enzyme molecule, like all globular proteins, is maintained by hydrogen bonds, ionic bonds and sometimes disulphide bonds between different parts of the polypeptide chain.

An enzyme molecule has an **active site**, the area to which the substrate can bind. The active site is precisely the right shape for the substrate molecule to slot into. Particular amino acids at the enzyme's active site have R groups that are able to form temporary bonds with the substrate. Different enzymes have different shapes of active sites, with different R groups in them, and so each kind of enzyme can only bind with particular substrates. For example, the enzyme amylase can only bind with polymers of α(1–4) glucose, that is starch or glycogen, and not with proteins. This property of enzymes is known as **enzyme specificity**.

How enzymes work

Most metabolic reactions will not take place unless provided with some energy. This energy is called **activation energy**.

Enzymes help reactions to happen by reducing activation energy.

For example, starch will not just break down into maltose unless you give it some energy. You can do this by heating a starch solution (plus a little acid) to almost boiling point for a few minutes. In your body, however, the enzyme amylase allows this reaction to take place without the addition of so much energy.

In a solution containing amylase molecules and starch molecules, both types of molecule are in constant motion. Some of the starch molecules will bump into the active sites of the amylase molecules, and temporary bonds will form between the substrate (starch) and the enzyme. As these bonds form, the starch molecules are pulled into a slightly different shape, which makes it easy for the glycosidic bonds between their glucose molecules to be broken. The bonds break, and the resulting maltose molecules move out of the active site (Fig 21).

Many enzymes have names ending with -ase, relating to the name of their substrate. Thus, amylase catalyses the hydrolysis of amylose. It is therefore very important that you write these words absolutely clearly, so that the examiner can tell when you are writing about the enzyme and when you are writing about its substrate.

Fig 21
How amylase catalyses the
hydrolysis of starch

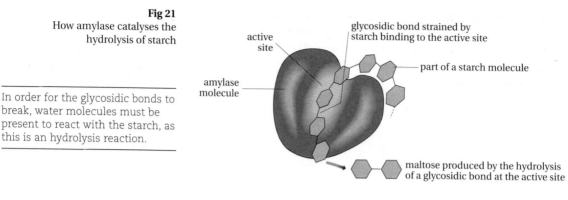

In order for the glycosidic bonds to break, water molecules must be present to react with the starch, as this is an hydrolysis reaction.

Most forms of amylase break down starch molecules to the disaccharide maltose, not individual glucose molecules. However, amylase from some kinds of fungi can convert starch directly to glucose.

The enzyme's active site is now free to receive another substrate molecule and catalyse another hydrolysis reaction. For most metabolic reactions the whole process, from the substrate binding to release of the products, takes place in a fraction of a second. So, just a very few enzyme molecules can catalyse the change of many substrate molecules to products in a very short time.

How temperature affects enzyme activity

Changes in temperature affect the rate of an enzyme-catalysed reaction in two ways.

The increase in rate of a reaction as temperature increases is true for many reactions, not only those catalysed by enzymes.

Firstly, at higher temperatures, all the molecules in a solution – including enzyme molecules and substrate molecules – move around faster than they do at lower temperatures. So reactions tend to take place faster, because the enzymes and substrates bump into each other more frequently and with more energy.

E Do not say that enzymes are 'killed' by high temperatures! Enzymes are just molecules, not living organisms, and you can't kill a molecule.

Secondly, high temperatures can cause enzyme molecules to lose their shape. At high temperatures the bonds that hold the tertiary structure of the enzyme molecule in shape tend to break. This is especially true of hydrogen bonds. When the active site of the enzyme molecule loses its shape, it is no longer able to bond with the substrate molecule, so the conversion of substrate to product cannot take place. The enzyme molecule is said to be **denatured**.

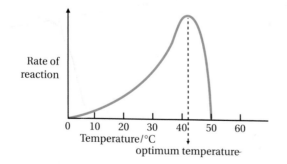

Fig 22
The effect of temperature on an enzyme-catalysed reaction

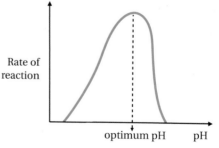

Fig 23
The effect of pH on an enzyme-catalysed reaction

The relationship between temperature and rate of reaction is shown in Fig 22. Notice that the first part of the curve rises exponentially (that is, in a curve of increasing steepness), while the second part drops even more steeply. The temperature at which the enzyme works most rapidly is called its **optimum temperature**. Plant enzymes often have optimum temperatures of around 25 °C. Enzymes that normally function inside the human body have optimums just above 37 °C, while those that are made by bacteria which live in hot springs can have optimums as high as 80 °C.

> The optimum temperature for an enzyme is the temperature at which it works fastest, but it is not the *best* temperature for it, because denaturation is probably beginning at this temperature.

How pH affects enzyme activity

The pH of a solution is a measure of how acidic or alkaline it is. The pH affects the ionisation of the R groups in any protein, including enzyme molecules. This affects the ionic bonds and hydrogen bonds that help to hold the enzyme molecule in its precise three-dimensional shape. Extremes of pH can therefore denature enzymes, and stop them functioning as catalysts (Fig 23).

> The pH scale runs from 1 to 14, where pH7 is neutral. A solution with a pH below 7 is acidic, while one with a pH above 7 is alkaline.

Many enzymes have an optimum pH of around 7 (neutral). However, some enzymes work in very acidic or very alkaline conditions. For example, the enzyme pepsin works in the stomach, where hydrochloric acid produces a very acidic solution. Pepsin has an optimum pH of 2.

The effects of enzyme and substrate concentration

So long as there are plenty of substrate molecules in a solution, then the more enzyme molecules there are the faster the reaction can take place. This is because it is more likely that a substrate molecule will bump into an enzyme's active site. So, increasing the enzyme concentration will increase the rate of the reaction (Fig 24). However, at *very* high enzyme concentrations there may not be enough substrate molecules to keep all the enzyme molecules busy all the time, so the graph eventually flattens out.

Similarly, so long as there are plenty of enzyme molecules in a solution, adding more substrate molecules will increase the chances of enzyme–substrate collisions, and so increase the rate of the reaction. However, unless the enzyme concentration is extremely high, there comes a point when every enzyme is working flat out, and cannot bind with substrate molecules any faster, however many there are. The curve therefore flattens out at high substrate concentrations (Fig 25).

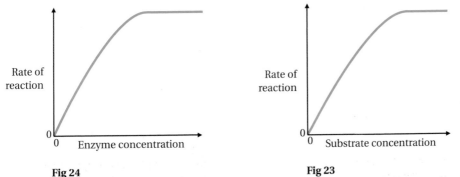

Fig 24
The effect of enzyme concentration on the rate of reaction

Fig 23
The effect of substrate concentration on the rate of reaction

Inhibitors

An enzyme inhibitor is a substance that slows down the rate at which an enzyme-catalysed reaction takes place. Many enzyme inhibitors work by binding with the enzyme, with the result that the enzyme can no longer bind with its substrate (Fig 26).

Fig 26
How inhibitors affect enzyme activity

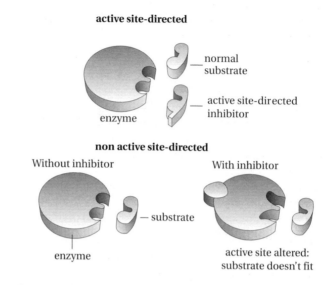

Some inhibitors have shapes rather like the enzyme's normal substrate molecule, allowing them to bind at the active site of the enzyme. They are called **active site-directed inhibitors**. If there is an inhibitor molecule in the active site, the substrate cannot bind there. Some active site-directed inhibitors bind permanently to the active site, so that they permanently inactivate the enzyme. Others bind temporarily. While the inhibitor is out of the active site, it is possible for a substrate molecule to slot in, so the inhibitor will not completely stop the reaction, just slow it down. The inhibitor and the substrate are competing for the active site, so these inhibitors are sometimes called **competitive inhibitors**. The chances of a substrate molecule getting into the active site depend on:

● the relative concentrations of substrate and inhibitor – the more substrate molecules there are compared to inhibitor molecules, the more likely it is that a substrate rather than an inhibitor will bind with the enzyme's active site.

● how long the inhibitor stays attached to the enzyme before moving away – the shorter the inhibitor–enzyme complex lasts, the more chance the substrate has to bind with the active site, and the less inhibition of the reaction.

Other inhibitors bind to parts of the enzyme other than the active site. They are called **non-active site-directed inhibitors**. They are completely different in shape from the substrate molecules, and they do not compete with them for the active site. They are sometimes called **non-competitive inhibitors**. They slow down, or even stop, the rate of reaction by causing the enzyme molecule to change shape when they bind with it. This distorts the active site, so that it can no longer bind effectively with a substrate molecule.

Commercial uses of enzymes

Enzymes are widely used in the food industry. One example is **pectinase**, which is used in the extraction of fruit juice. The fruit is crushed to a pulp, and pectinase is added. Pectinase breaks down **pectin**, a substance found in plant cell walls. This allows a greater volume of juice to be extracted from a given quantity of fruit pulp. The pectinase can also help to produce a clearer, less cloudy juice. If the fruit contains acid, for example oranges, then a pectinase with a low optimum pH is used.

Biological detergents contain a variety of enzymes, including **proteases**. Proteases digest proteins. Dirt on clothes often contains proteins, such as food stains, sweat marks or blood. The proteases hydrolyse proteins to smaller polypeptides or amino acids, which are soluble and so dissolve in the water in which the clothes are being washed. The proteases that are used in washing powders are often extracted from bacteria that survive in high temperatures, such as in hot springs. These thermophilic bacteria produce enzymes with very high optimum temperatures, so washing powders containing these enzymes can be used at relatively high temperatures without denaturing them.

In the two examples above, the enzymes are used in solution. However, in many industrial processes the enzymes are **immobilised**. This means that they are fixed to some kind of support, such as beads of alginate jelly. For example, the enzyme **lactase** may be immobilised in this way.

Lactase digests the disaccharide lactose to glucose and galactose. Lactose is found in milk, but many people have no enzymes in their digestive system that can digest it, and so require milk products that are free from lactose. Milk is passed through columns of alginate beads containing lactase, so that the milk emerging from the columns contains glucose and galactose, but no lactose. The lactase molecules remain fixed to the alginate beads. This has several advantages over simply mixing the lactase with the milk:

This process is also used to make glucose and galactose from the lactose in whey left over from cheese-making. These monosaccharides are much sweeter than lactose, and are used to make confectionery.

- the lactase molecules are not lost with the product, and so can be used over and over again; this is especially important if the enzyme is an expensive one

- the product is enzyme-free, and needs no further processing to remove lactase from it

- immobilised enzymes are less susceptible to denaturation by changes in temperature or pH.

3 Cellular organisation

All living organisms – except viruses – are made of cells. There are two basic cell types:

- small and relatively simple **prokaryotic** cells, such as bacteria
- **eukaryotic** cells, such as plant, animal and fungal cells.

Prokaryotic cells

A prokaryotic cell has no nucleus or other membrane-bound organelles. The cell of the bacterium *Escherichia coli* is an example of a typical prokaryotic cell (Fig 27).

Fig 27
The structure of a bacterial cell illustrated by *Escherichia coli*

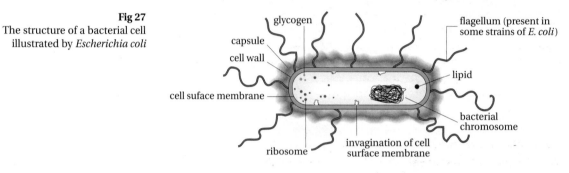

Table 4
Components of a prokaryotic cell

NB also INVAGINATIONS!

Cell feature	Description
cell wall	The cell wall of bacteria is not made of cellulose, but of a variety of other polysaccharides including **peptidoglycans**. The cell wall is rigid and strong, and protects the bacterium from bursting if it absorbs water. It is fully permeable.
cell surface (plasma) membrane	This is a partially permeable membrane, that controls the movement of substances between the cell and its environment. It may be folded in places, providing a large surface area on which the enzymes involved in reactions such as aerobic respiration may be situated.
capsule	This is a protective layer of slime.
flagella	Flagella (singular: flagellum) are used for movement. There is a motor at the base of each flagellum, in the cytoplasm, that can make the flagellum rotate, moving the bacterium rather as a propeller moves a boat.
bacterial chromosome	The DNA in a bacterial cell is a long, double helix forming a circular molecule. There are no histones associated with it as there are in eukaryotic cells, so it does not form a true chromosome. The DNA is not contained within a nucleus. The bacterial chromosome carries the instructions for making proteins within the cell.

Both prokaryotic and eukaryotic cells can have flagella, but the structure is completely different in the two types of cell.

Table 4 (continued)
Components of a proka ll

Cell feature	Description
plasmids	These are small, circular DNA molecules. Each bacterial cell may have several tiny plasmids, as well as its much larger bacterial chromosome. There are many different types of plasmids, and they often carry genes for characteristics such as antibiotic resistance. Plasmids can be passed from one bacterium to another, even to different species. Plasmids are frequently used in gene technology for transferring genes from one cell to another.
glycogen granules	These form an insoluble store of carbohydrate, which can be broken down to provide glucose for use as a respiratory substrate.
lipid droplets	These are an insoluble energy store.
ribosomes	This is where polypeptides and proteins are formed, following the code on the DNA molecule. Ribosomes in prokaryotic cells are smaller than those in eukaryotic cells.

Eukaryotic cells

Eukaryotic means 'true nucleus', and these cells all have a double membrane, or **nuclear envelope**, which surrounds an area containing the DNA. Plant and animal cells (Figs 28 and 29) are two types of eukaryotic cells.

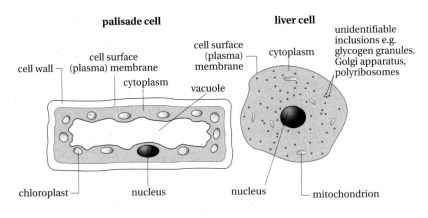

Fig 28
The structure of a leaf palisade cell and a liver cell as revealed by **light microscopy**

Fig 29
The structure of a leaf palisade cell and a liver cell as revealed by **electron microscopy**

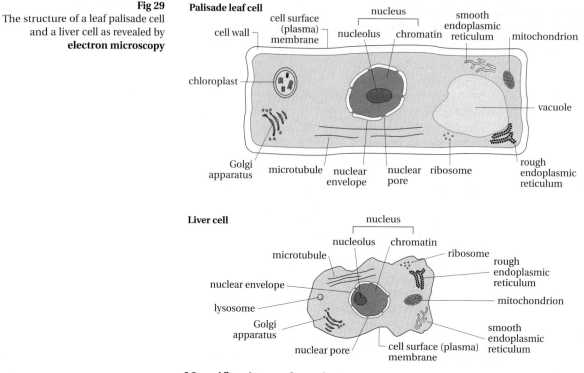

Magnification and resolution

> The magnification of an image is a measure of how many times larger it is than the real size of the object. Magnification is a ratio, and so has no units.
>
> $$magnification = \frac{size\ of\ image}{size\ of\ object}$$
>
> The resolution of an image is the minimum distance apart that two tiny points can be, and still be distinguished as two separate points. If resolution is high, the image looks sharp and a lot of detail can be seen.

There is no limit on how much either a light microscope or an electron microscope can magnify a specimen. The magnification depends on the strength of the lenses used, and there is nothing to stop you placing a lens on top of a light microscope that throws a huge image on the wall. However, in all optical systems resolution *does* have an upper limit, and if the resolution of the image is poor then all you will see is an enormous blur.

The limit of resolution of a really good light microscope is about 200 nm. Any objects smaller than 200 nm will not be visible, or will just look like a blur. Any objects closer together than 200 nm will appear to be one object. However, the limit of resolution of an electron microscope is 0.5 nm. So an electron microscope can pick out objects that are 400 times smaller than those visible with a light microscope.

Limit of resolution

a) *Light microscope = 200nm*

b) *Electron microscope = 0.5 nm*

Electron microscopes have a higher resolution than light microscopes because electron beams have a much shorter wavelength than light. The limit of resolution is about 0.45 times the wavelength.

Components of a eukaryotic cell

The structures found inside a cell are called **organelles**. Unless otherwise stated, the structures described below are found in both plant and animal cells.

Cell feature	Description
nucleus	The nucleus is the membrane-bound region of the cell that contains the DNA.
chromosomes	In a eukaryotic cell, the DNA is in the form of a number of linear molecules, each of which has proteins called **histones** associated with it. Each molecule and its histones is called a chromosome. When the cell is not dividing, the chromosomes are not visible as threads, but form dark and light areas called **chromatin**. When the cell begins to divide, the chromosomes curl up to form shorter, thicker structures that can be seen with a light microscope.
nuclear envelope	The nucleus is surrounded by a double membrane called the nuclear envelope. This keeps the DNA away from the rest of the activities going on in the cell. There are pores in the envelope that allow mRNA to pass out into the cytoplasm.
nucleolus	This is a darkly-staining area of the nucleus, where ribosomal RNA is being made by transcription from DNA.
rough endoplasmic reticulum (RER)	RER is a network of membranes running throughout the cytoplasm, forming a system of interconnecting compartments called **cisternae**. It is called 'rough' because ribosomes are attached to the outer surfaces of the membranes. Proteins are made on these ribosomes. Some of the proteins pass into the cisternae, which can break up into small vesicles and transport the proteins to other parts of the cell such as the Golgi apparatus.
smooth endoplasmic reticulum (SER)	SER has a similar structure to RER, but without the ribosomes. SER is the site of synthesis of cholesterol and steroid hormones.
Golgi apparatus	This is a stack of curved cisternae, where proteins made on the RER are packaged and modified ready for export from the cell. Vesicles move from the RER and become part of the convex face of the Golgi apparatus. Inside, the proteins may have carbohydrates added to them, to form glycoproteins. Vesicles containing the modified proteins break away from the concave face of the Golgi apparatus, and move towards the plasma membrane. They fuse with the membrane in a process called **exocytosis**, liberating their contents outside the cell.

Table 5
Components of a eukaryotic cell

Protein synthesis is described on page 17.

Exocytosis is described on page 35.

Table 5 (*continued*)
Components of a eukaryotic cell

Cell feature	Description
lysosomes *Animal only*	Lysosomes are vesicles, containing hydrolytic (digestive) enzymes, that break away from the Golgi apparatus. Lysosomes can break down substances brought into the cell by phagocytosis (such as a bacterium), or unwanted organelles inside the cell. The membrane of the lysosome fuses with the membrane around the bacterium or the organelle, releasing its enzymes onto it. Lysosomes are found in animal cells, but not plant cells.
ribosomes	These are small structures, made of ribosomal RNA (rRNA) and protein, that provide a site for the synthesis of proteins and also help with the mechanism of this process. If many ribosomes are all working on the same mRNA strand, then they appear as a group called a **polyribosome.**
mitochondria	Mitochondria (singular: mitochondrion) are the sites of aerobic respiration, in which oxygen is used to release energy from organic molecules and make ATP. A mitochondrion has a double membrane (Fig 30). The inner membrane is folded to form **cristae**, which provide a large surface area on which some of the stages of respiration take place. Mitochondria contain their own DNA and ribosomes, so they are able to make some proteins.
chlorōplasts *Plant only*	Like mitochondria, chloroplasts have a double membrane (Fig 31). Chloroplasts are found only in certain types of plant cells. They are the sites of photosynthesis, in which light energy is used to make carbohydrates from carbon dioxide and water. They contain membranes called **lamellae**, which are folded to form sacs called **thylakoids**. These stack together to form **grana**. Chlorophyll molecules are embedded in the lamellae. Chloroplasts often contain starch grains. Like mitochondria, they contain their own DNA and ribosomes.
microtubules	Every cell contains tiny, hollow cylinders called **microtubules** that are found throughout the cytoplasm. Microtubules are made of a protein called **tubulin**. They help other organelles to move from place to place within the cell. The spindle fibres that form during cell division, described on pages 38 to 41, are microtubules.
centrioles *Animal only*	Animal cells, but not plant cells, contain two centrioles that are usually positioned just outside the nuclear envelope. The centrioles lie at right angles to each other. They divide just before cell division, and help to produce and organise the microtubules that form the spindle fibres (see page 40).

ATP is the energy currency of the cell. It is used to fuel all the energy-requiring processes, and each cell has to make its own ATP.

chloroplast double membrane = chloroplast envelope

Table 5 (continued)
Components of a eukaryotic cell

Cell feature	Description
cellulose cell wall *Plant only.*	Plant cells, but not animal cells, have a tough, protective cell wall that surrounds the entire cell, outside the plasma membrane. The cell wall is made of fibres of cellulose embedded in a matrix (background material) of pectin and other materials. The cellulose fibres are very strong, and are often arranged in layers in which the fibres lie in different directions. This composite structure is extremely resistant to extension or compression, so the plant cell wall provides strength and protection. For example, it prevents a plant cell from expanding too far and bursting when water is taken up. The cell wall is fully permeable, and plays no part in controlling what can enter and leave the cell.
cell membranes	Many organelles inside a cell are either *made* of membranes (for example the endoplasmic reticulum) or are *surrounded* by membranes (for example mitochondria). The whole cell is also surrounded by a membrane, called the **plasma membrane** or **cell surface membrane**. All of these membranes have a similar structure, shown in Fig 32. They are all able to control what passes through them, and also serve as attachment sites for enzymes and other molecules. The membranes inside a cell help to divide it into different compartments, within which different metabolic reactions can take place without interfering with one another.

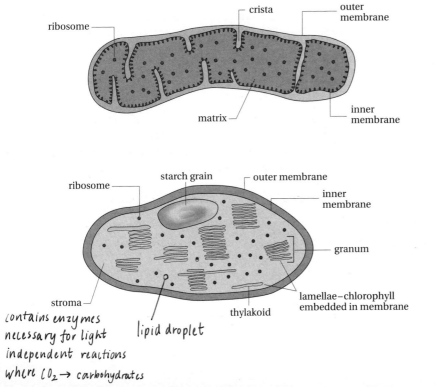

Fig 30
A mitochondrion

ribosome — crista — outer membrane — matrix — inner membrane

Fig 31
A chloroplast

ribosome — starch grain — outer membrane — inner membrane — granum — stroma — thylakoid — lamellae–chlorophyll embedded in membrane — lipid droplet

contains enzymes necessary for light independent reactions where $CO_2 \rightarrow$ carbohydrates

Prokaryotic cell	Eukaryotic cell
bacteria are prokaryotic	plants, animals and fungi have this type of cell
does not contain membrane-bound organelles	contains membrane-bound organelles
smaller ribosomes	larger ribosomes
circular DNA, with no histones	linear DNA, associated with histones
DNA free in cytoplasm; no nucleus	DNA confined to nucleus, bounded by nuclear envelope

The structure of the cell surface membrane

The cell surface (plasma) membrane is made up of a bilayer of phospholipid molecules, in which protein molecules float (Fig 32). There are also cholesterol molecules in amongst the phospholipids. It is said to be a **fluid mosaic** structure, because the molecules move around within it ('fluid') and because it would look rather like a mosaic pattern if you could view it from above. The membrane is only about 7 nm thick.

All of the membranes within a cell have a structure similar to the cell surface membrane.

Fig 32
The cell surface membrane

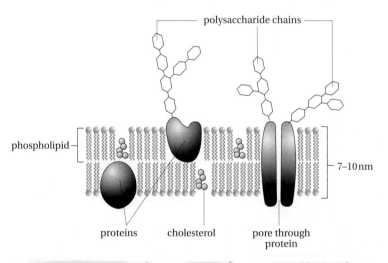

The **phospholipid bilayer** forms a barrier to most water-soluble substances. However, substances with small molecules, such as oxygen and carbon dioxide, can diffuse freely through it. So can lipid-soluble molecules, such as alcohol. The bilayer also contains **cholesterol** molecules, which help to maintain the fluidity of the membrane.

The **proteins** which are embedded in the bilayer have a variety of functions. Many of these proteins have carbohydrate chains attached to them, forming composite molecules called **glycoproteins**. Their functions include:

- **receptors** – the carbohydrate chains may act as receptors for other molecules, such as hormones. For example, liver cells contain glycoprotein molecules in their membranes that are able to combine with insulin molecules. So liver cells respond to insulin, while other kinds of cells that lack these receptors do not.

- **channels** – some of the proteins have **hydrophilic** channels running through them. This allows water-soluble substances to pass through the membrane and is described in the next section.

Transport across membranes

On each side of any cell surface membrane, there will be a solution of many substances dissolved in water. Molecules and ions in solution are in constant motion. Some of them will bump into the membrane, and may be able to pass through to the other side. If they do this with no input of metabolic energy from the cell, then they are said to move **passively**. If the cell provides energy to move the molecules or ions across the membrane, then the movement is **active.**

Passive methods of transport include:

- diffusion

- facilitated diffusion

- osmosis.

Active methods of transport include:

- active transport

- endocytosis

- exocytosis.

Diffusion

Molecules and ions can diffuse across membranes if they are soluble in lipids. As they move around randomly, some of them hit the phospholipid bilayer, and are able to pass through it. If there are more of a particular type of molecule on one side of the membrane than the other, more of them will hit the membrane on that side. Although molecules will go both ways across the membrane, the chances are that the net (overall) movement will be from the side where their concentration is higher. Diffusion happens down a concentration gradient (Fig 33).

It is important to realise that diffusion is purely a result of the *random* movement of molecules or ions. The molecules or ions do not purposefully move down a concentration gradient. Nor does the cell do anything at all to make it happen.

Fig 33
Diffusion

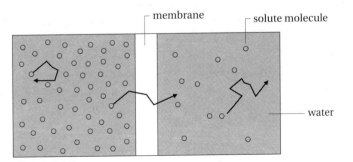

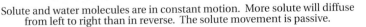

Solute and water molecules are in constant motion. More solute will diffuse from left to right than in reverse. The solute movement is passive.

The rate of diffusion across a cell surface membrane is affected by:

KE

- **temperature** – the higher the temperature, the faster the molecules and ions are moving, so the faster they diffuse.

- **concentration gradient** – the greater the difference in concentration on either side of the membrane, the greater the difference in the number of molecules or ions moving in each direction, so the greater the net rate of diffusion.

- **the surface area of the membrane** – the greater the surface area, the more frequently a molecule or ion will hit it and be able to pass through.

- **the nature of the substance diffusing** – small molecules diffuse faster than large ones, and ones that are very soluble in lipids diffuse faster than those that are not so lipid-soluble.

Facilitated diffusion

'Facilitated' means 'made easier' – the channel proteins make it easier for certain substances to diffuse through the membrane.

It is still possible for substances to diffuse across membranes even if they are not soluble in lipids. They pass through proteins that have channels in them that are just the right shape and size to allow particular molecules or ions to travel through. In some cases, the molecules or ions just pass through a 'hole' in the protein, while in others the protein changes shape to allow the molecule or ion to pass through (Fig 34). In neither case does the cell use any metabolic energy to move the substances through – the molecules are simply diffusing down their concentration gradients.

The rate of facilitated diffusion therefore depends on the four factors described for 'ordinary' diffusion, and also on the number of channel proteins in the membrane. Moreover, the channel proteins may be able to open and close their channels, and so the rate of facilitated diffusion also depends on the proportion of the protein channels that are open.

Fig 34
Facilitated diffusion

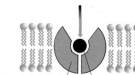

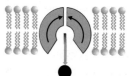

carrier protein�molecule/ion
In this case facilitated diffusion uses a carrier protein. The diffusing molecule combines with the carrier protein, causing a shift in shape which moves the molecule through the channel.

open   closed

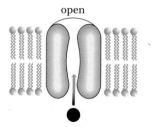

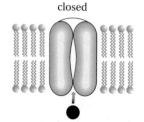

In this case a protein with a pore spans the membrane. Ions such as Ca^{2+} pass through the protein pore.

The protein changes shape, so the pore becomes too narrow to allow ions through.

Osmosis

Osmosis (Fig 35) is the diffusion of water through a partially permeable membrane. A partially permeable membrane is one that lets some substances, such as water molecules move through freely, but prevents the movement of others. Cell membranes are partially permeable membranes. Osmosis is so important to cells that special terminology is used to describe how and why the water moves.

Remember to make it clear in answers to questions about osmosis that only *water molecules* are moving across the membrane, not the *whole solution*. **E**

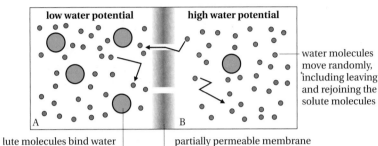

low water potential high water potential

water molecules move randomly, including leaving and rejoining the solute molecules

A B

lute molecules bind water
lower the water potential

partially permeable membrane
(permeable to water but not to all solutes)

'ith fewer solute molecules on the right, the water potential is higher so more water diffuses from right to left than from left to right.

Fig 35
Osmosis

If you remember that water diffuses from a solution with a high water potential to a solution with a low water potential, you will be able to answer most examination questions about osmosis! **E**

Just as for any kind of diffusion, water molecules tend to diffuse down their concentration gradient. However, we do not usually talk about the 'concentration' of water molecules, because the normal meaning of the word concentration is to describe how much solute there is in a solution. Moreover, the tendency of water to diffuse into or out of a solution depends not only on how much water there is in it, but also what pressure that solution is under. So the term **water potential** is used instead.

A solution is a mixture of a solute (for example sucrose) in a solvent (for example water).

A frequently used shorthand for 'water potential' is the Greek letter ψ (psi), pronounced 'sye'.

> *You can think of the water potential of a solution as being the tendency for water to diffuse out of it.* **D**

$$\psi_{cell} = \psi_{(solute)} + \psi_{(pressure)}$$

The water potential of a solution is determined by:

- the concentration of solute that is dissolved in it – the higher the concentration of solute, the lower the water potential.

- the pressure that the solution is under – the higher the pressure on the solution, then the higher the water potential.

If you think carefully about it, this is all very logical. If there is a solution with a high concentration of solute on side A of a membrane, and a solution with a low concentration of solute on side B, then there are more water molecules on side B than side A. So you would expect the water to diffuse from side B to side A. Side A has the higher concentration of solute, so it has the lower water potential – the water is going to diffuse from the high water potential to the low water potential, down its water potential gradient.

By convention, the water potential of pure water at normal atmospheric pressure is 0. So if solute is dissolved in the water, making its water potential lower, then the water potential of the solution has a negative value. Remember that −20 is a lower number than −2!

Water potential is measured in kilopascals (kPa), which are units of pressure.

Similarly, if you imagine pressing down on a solution on one side of the membrane, and not on the other side, then you'd expect the extra pressure to 'push' water molecules from the 'high pressure' side to the 'low pressure' side. So the water will tend to diffuse from the side where the pressure is high (high water potential) to the side where it is low (low water potential).

Active transport

Active transport (Fig 36) differs from the methods of passive transport described above because:

- it involves the use of metabolic energy by the cell

- substances are made to move *against* their concentration gradient.

Active transport depends on particular glycoproteins in the cell surface membrane called **carriers** or **transporters**. There are many different kinds of carrier molecules, because each kind has a particular shape that is specific to the molecules or ions that it transports.

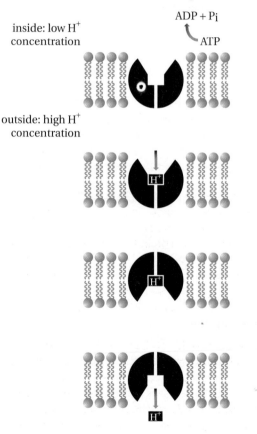

Fig 36
An example of active transport. The H^+-ATPase pump removes hydrogen ions from a cell against a concentration gradient. It is found in the membrane of the kidney tubule cells, where it contributes to the production of acidic urine. The breakdown of ATP provides the energy for the movement of H^+.

Cells produce ATP by respiration, so if respiration is prevented then active transport stops. Cells that are involved in active transport often have especially large numbers of mitochondria, to provide ATP.

For example, plant roots are able to take up nitrate ions from the soil, even though the concentration of nitrate ions in the soil is lower than that inside the root. The cell membranes of the root hair cells contain carrier proteins for nitrate ions. When a nitrate ion bumps into it, the carrier protein changes shape, using energy provided by ATP, in such a way that it pushes the nitrate ion into the cell.

Endocytosis and exocytosis

Diffusion, including facilitated diffusion and osmosis, and active transport all involve the movement of molecules and ions individually – one at a time – through the membrane. Endocytosis and exocytosis, however, move substances in bulk into and out of the cell.

Endocytosis (Fig 37) brings solids or bulk liquids into a cell, while exocytosis exports them from the cell.

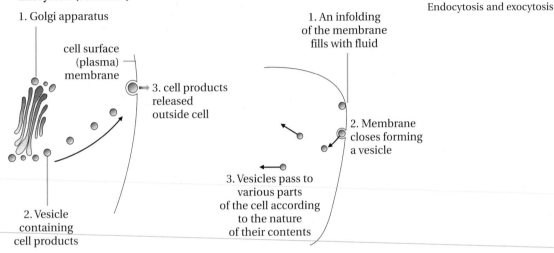

Exocytosis (secretion)

1. Golgi apparatus

cell surface (plasma) membrane

3. cell products released outside cell

2. Vesicle containing cell products

Fig 37
Endocytosis and exocytosis

1. An infolding of the membrane fills with fluid

2. Membrane closes forming a vesicle

3. Vesicles pass to various parts of the cell according to the nature of their contents

Endocytosis (pinocytosis or phagocytosis)

In endocytosis, the cell surface membrane encloses the substance, forming a small compartment called a **vesicle**. This happens in phagocytes, for example – the white blood cells that are responsible for engulfing and destroying bacteria. In this case, the endocytotic vesicle will fuse with lysosomes inside the cell, and the hydrolytic enzymes from the lysosome will digest the bacterium. When endocytosis involves the take-up of solid objects such as a bacterium, it is also known as **phagocytosis**. If it involves the take-up of liquids, often in lots of tiny vesicles instead of one larger one, it is known as **pinocytosis**.

In exocytosis, a vesicle containing whatever is to be removed from the cell moves towards the cell surface membrane and fuses with it. The contents are therefore released outside the cell. If the substance that is released has a useful function outside the cell – for example, it might be digestive enzymes that are being released into the alimentary canal – the process is known as **secretion**. Very often, the vesicles originate from the Golgi body.

Aggregations of cells

In multicellular organisms, cells do not work individually but in coordination with one another. An organism such as yourself or a plant contains many different types of cells, each specialised for a particular range of functions. These cells are usually grouped to form **tissues.**

D A tissue is a group of cells that have a common origin and a common function. Frequently, the cells in a tissue all have a similar structure, although this is not always the case.

Fig 38
A cross-section through a leaf

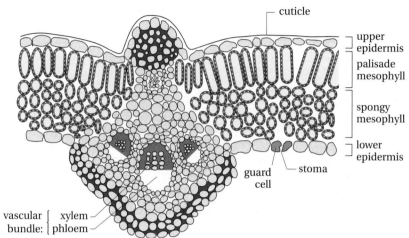

For example, a leaf (Fig 38) contains a number of different tissues: epidermis, palisade and spongy mesophyll, xylem and phloem tissues.

The **epidermis** is made up of a single layer of cells which secrete a layer of wax, called the cuticle, onto their outer surface. This waxy layer is usually thicker on the upper surface than on the lower, as its main function is to prevent water loss from the leaf; sunlight warms the upper surface more than the lower and, therefore, evaporation is more likely to occur from this upper surface. The cells of the epidermis have no chloroplasts, and so do not photosynthesise. The only exception to this is the **guard cells**, found mostly in the lower epidermis, whose role is to control the opening and closure of the space between them, called a **stoma.** This regulates the entry and exit of the gases carbon dioxide, oxygen and water vapour.

The **palisade mesophyll** is made up of one or more layers of tall, relatively narrow cells containing abundant chloroplasts. The cells are quite closely packed, with only small air spaces between them. This is the main photosynthetic tissue in the leaf.

The **spongy mesophyll** lies beneath the palisade mesophyll. It, too, contains chloroplasts and photosynthesises, but to a lesser extent than the palisade mesophyll. There are extensive air spaces between the cells, which connect with the stomata. These air spaces allow carbon dioxide to diffuse easily to the palisade mesophyll cells, for use in photosynthesis. The numerous air spaces mean that the total surface area of the spongy mesophyll cells in contact with the air is large, and significant amounts of water evaporate from their cell walls into the air spaces. This is the source of the water vapour that diffuses out of the stomata in the process of transpiration. The loss of water from these cells reduces the water potential in them. This provides the water potential gradient that draws water all the way up through the plant from its roots, thus maintaining a supply of water for photosynthesis and mineral ions to the leaves. The evaporation of water also helps to keep the leaves cool.

The **xylem tissue** is made up of a number of different types of cells, including **xylem elements**. These are long, dead, hollow cells whose cell walls contain **lignin**. They have no end walls, and are joined end to end in continuous columns called **xylem vessels**. Xylem vessels conduct water from the roots up to the leaves.

Phloem tissue is also made up of several different types of cells. These include **sieve tube elements**, which are elongated cells with cellulose cell walls, and living contents. However, they have no nucleus and relatively few organelles. Their end walls are perforated to form **sieve plates**. Sieve tube elements, like xylem elements, lie end to end to form long columns which are called **sieve tubes**. These are responsible for the transport of organic substances that the plant has made, such as sucrose. These substances are often called **assimilates** and their transport is called **translocation**.

In a leaf, the xylem tissue and phloem tissue lie closely together to form **vascular bundles**, which make up the veins.

A structure such as a leaf, that is made up of an aggregation of tissues, is known as an **organ**. The bodies of animals are also made up of organs, such as the liver or the eye.

Interphase

G_1 — Cell may be active: growing, synthesising, secreting etc but no special processes associated with cell division take place

S — Nucleic acids are synthesised & chloroplasts /mitochondria replicate (along with other organelles)

G_2 — resting stage ATP reserves built up

G_0 — Cell stops dividing. Maturity reached.

4 The cell cycle

Mammals, such as yourself, begin their lives as a single cell. This cell divides to form two cells, and these in turn divide repeatedly to form four, eight, sixteen and so on. In later stages of development, most cells no longer divide, although some – such as those at the base of the epidermis in the skin – continue dividing throughout your life. The cells pass through repeated phases of resting and division, resting and division. One complete phase is called the **cell cycle** (Figs 39 and 40).

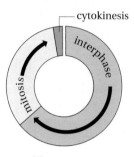

Fig 39
The cell cycle

During **interphase** the cell grows, and replication of DNA takes place.

During **mitosis** the nucleus divides into two nuclei, each containing a complete and identical set of chromosomes.

During **cytokinesis** cytoplasm divides to form two genetically identical cells.

Fig 40
Changes in DNA mass during the cell cycle

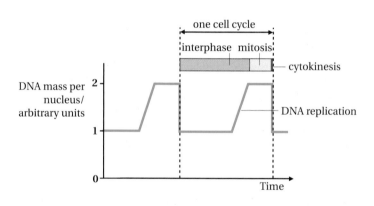

This sequence of events takes place in all multicellular organisms, not only mammals. In plants, for example, mitotic cell cycles take place repeatedly in the growing regions such as the root tips and shoot tips.

Significance of the mitotic cell cycle

The events of the mitotic cell cycle result in the production of new cells that are genetically identical to the parent cell. To summarise, mitosis:

- is the type of nuclear division that takes place whenever growth and replacement of cells is taking place, and during asexual reproduction

- produces new cells which contain exactly the same genes, with exactly the same base sequences, as the parent cell

- involves the exact and equal division of chromosomes, so that each daughter cell has precisely the same number and type of chromosomes as its parent cell.

There is another type of nuclear division in which each daughter cell acquires only half of the original number of chromosomes, and in which these chromosomes are not identical with those of the parent cell. This division is called **meiosis**, and it only occurs during sexual reproduction.

Chromosomes

Chromosome number

Different organisms have different numbers of chromosomes in the nuclei of their cells. Humans, for example, have 46 chromosomes, while garlic (*Allium sativum*) has 16 and an oak tree (*Quercus robur*) has 24.

The fact that all of these numbers are even numbers is no coincidence. All of these organisms are **diploid** – that is, they have two copies of each type of chromosome in their cells. Humans have 23 types of chromosome, garlic 8 and oak trees 12. A diploid cell, such as a liver cell in a human or a leaf cell in a garlic plant, has *two* complete sets of chromosomes, two of each type.

The number of chromosomes in a single set – that is, one of each type – is called the **haploid chromosome number**. The shorthand symbol for this is **n**. So, for a human n = 23, for garlic n = 8 and for an oak tree n = 12.

The number of chromosomes in a double set – that is, the number found in most cells in an adult organism – is called the **diploid chromosome number**. The shorthand symbol for this is **2n**. So, for a human 2n = 46, for garlic 2n = 16 and for an oak tree 2n = 24.

Differentiation

Most organisms begin as a single cell that divides repeatedly to produce all the cells in the adult organism. These divisions are all by mitosis, so every cell in an organism has exactly the same chromosomes in its nuclei. However, cells develop, or **differentiate**, into different types depending on their position in the organism. This happens because different genes are activated in different types of cells. Thus, although all the cells in an oak tree have 24 chromosomes and so contain the same genes, the palisade cells in a leaf have different genes switched on than the cells in the epidermis.

Chromosome structure

A chromosome (Fig 41) is a DNA molecule associated with proteins called **histones**. During interphase, just before mitosis is about to take place, each DNA molecule undergoes replication to produce an identical copy of itself. The two copies remain attached to each other, and are called **chromatids**. So, at this stage of the cell cycle, each chromosome is made up of two identical chromatids, sometimes called **sister chromatids**. They are held together at a region known as the **centromere**.

Fig 41
The structure of a chromosome prior to cell division

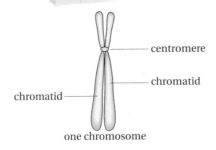

centromere

chromatid

chromatid

one chromosome

The events of mitosis separate the chromatids in each chromosome, and distribute them equally into the daughter cells.

Mitosis

Mitosis is a continuous series of events. However, it is convenient to consider it as four stages, which take place in the sequence shown in Fig 42.

Fig 42
Mitosis

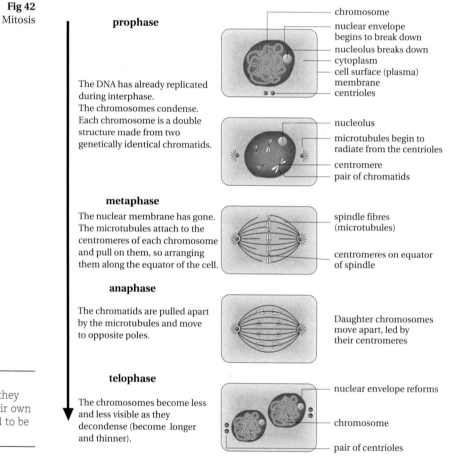

prophase

The DNA has already replicated during interphase.
The chromosomes condense.
Each chromosome is a double structure made from two genetically identical chromatids.

chromosome
nuclear envelope begins to break down
nucleolus breaks down
cytoplasm
cell surface (plasma) membrane
centrioles

nucleolus
microtubules begin to radiate from the centrioles
centromere
pair of chromatids

metaphase

The nuclear membrane has gone.
The microtubules attach to the centromeres of each chromosome and pull on them, so arranging them along the equator of the cell.

spindle fibres (microtubules)

centromeres on equator of spindle

anaphase

The chromatids are pulled apart by the microtubules and move to opposite poles.

Daughter chromosomes move apart, led by their centromeres

Once the chromatids have separated from each other, they each have an identity in their own right, and can be considered to be *chromosomes*.

telophase

The chromosomes become less and less visible as they decondense (become longer and thinner).

nuclear envelope reforms

chromosome

pair of centrioles

Usually, the cell now continues directly into the next stage of the cell cycle, **cytokinesis**. The cytoplasm divides into two, thus forming two daughter cells.

Mitosis and asexual reproduction

Asexual reproduction is the production of new organisms from a single parent, by processes that do not involve gametes or fertilisation.

In asexual reproduction, the cells that make up the new organism are derived from the parent by mitosis. The new organism, therefore, inherits all of its genetic information directly from its parent. Its cells have exactly the same number and type of chromosomes as the parent. Thus organisms produced by asexual reproduction are genetically identical to their parent and to each other. They are said to be **clones**, and asexual reproduction is sometimes known as cloning.

Cloning happens naturally in many organisms, both animals and plants, although it is much more common in plants. For example, in mammals the production of identical twins is an example of cloning. Many plants reproduce asexually. For example, brambles (blackberries) will form new plants where the stems bend over and touch the ground.

Artificial cloning of plants is carried out in a number of ways. Traditional methods include taking cuttings. A more recently developed technique is tissue culture, or micro-propagation. Here, tiny groups of cells are grown in a culture medium containing plant growth substances that induce them to develop into entire plants. This is a relatively cheap way of producing large numbers of genetically identical plants.

The zygote from which the identical twins develop was produced by sexual reproduction. The cloning occurs when the zygote divides by mitosis to form two genetically identical embryos.

AS1 Molecules and cells Sample unit test

1. The table below gives descriptions of organelles found in eukaryotic cells. Complete the table by writing the name of each organelle in the spaces provided.

Description	Name of organelle
Usually rod-shaped, 1 µm wide and up to 7 µm long; have double membrane; the inner membrane is folded to form cristae	
Rounded organelle approximately 25 nm in diameter; consists of RNA and protein	
Disc-shaped structure, about 1 µm wide and up to 5 µm long; contains a system of thylakoids	
Hollow, cylindrical structure; consists of nine triplets of microtubules	
Contains the genetic material of a cell; surrounded by a double membrane	

(Total 5 marks)

2. The diagram below shows the general structure of a phospholipid.

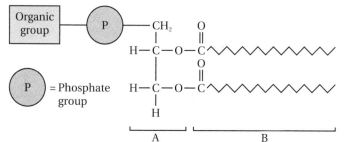

(a)   (i) Name the parts labelled A and B.

A ....

B ....

(2 marks)

(ii) Name the type of reaction by which the bonds between parts A and B may be broken.

....

(1 mark)

(b)   Phospholipids are major components of cell membranes. Explain how the properties of phospholipids are important in membrane formation.

....

....

....

....

(3 marks)

(Total 6 marks)

3. Distinguish between the following pairs of terms.

(a)   prokaryotic cell and eukaryotic cell

....

....

....

(3 marks)

(b)   fibrous protein and globular protein

....

....

....

(3 marks)

(Total 6 marks)

4. Read through the following passage on the cell cycle and mitosis, then write on the dotted lines the most appropriate word or words to complete the passage.

In the cell cycle, replication of DNA takes place during ....

At the beginning of prophase the chromosomes become visible and can be seen to

consist of two .... joined at the ....

The .... and nuclear membrane disappear and a spindle develops in the cell.

The chromosomes become attached to the spindle at the equator during

.... At anaphase one copy of each chromosome is pulled towards each

.... of the spindle. The final phase, called telophase, involves

the formation of two new nuclei.

(Total 6 marks)

5. The diagram below shows part of a messenger RNA (mRNA) molecule.

U   A   C   C   G   A   C   C   U   U   A   A

(a)   (i) How many codons are shown in this section of mRNA?

....

(1 mark)

(ii) What is specified by a sequence of codons in an mRNA molecule?

....

(1 mark)

(b)   A tRNA molecule carries a complementary base sequence for a particular codon.

(i) Write the complementary sequence for the first codon in the mRNA sequence given above.

....

(1 mark)

(ii) Describe the role of tRNA molecules in the process of protein synthesis.

....

....

....

....

(3 marks)

(Total 6 marks)

6. The diagram below shows the structure of part of a molecule of deoxyribonucleic acid (DNA).

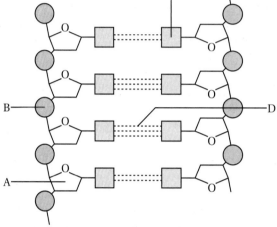

(a) Name the parts labelled A, B, C and D.

A ....

B ....

C ....

D ....

(4 marks)

(b) (i) On the diagram, draw a ring around one nucleotide. **(1 mark)**

(ii) What type of chemical reaction is involved in the formation of a molecule of DNA from nucleotides?

....

(1 mark)

(Total 6 marks)

7. The monosaccharides glucose and fructose are reducing sugars. Sucrose is a disaccharide which is not a reducing sugar.

The Benedict's test is used to detect reducing sugars. When reducing sugars are boiled with Benedict's solution a red precipitate is produced. This precipitate can be filtered from the solution, dried and weighed. If excess

Benedict's solution is used, the mass of precipitate produced is proportional to the concentration of reducing sugar in the solution. The enzyme sucrase is a hydrolase and does not react with Benedict's solution.

(a)   In an experiment, sucrase was added to a solution of sucrose and incubated for five minutes. The Benedict's test was then carried out on the resulting solution and a red precipitate was produced.

Suggest an explanation for this result.

....

....

....

(2 marks)

(b)   A further experiment was carried out to investigate the effect of silver nitrate on the activity of sucrase. The procedure described above was repeated, but different concentrations of silver nitrate were added to the sucrase. The solutions were kept at the same pH for the same time. The mass of precipitate produced by the Benedict's test at each concentration was measured. The results are shown in the table below.

Concentration of silver nitrate / mol dm^{-3}	Mass of precipitate / mg
0 (control)	50
10^{-6}	37
10^{-5}	27
10^{-4}	10

(i)   Calculate the percentage decrease in the mass of precipitate produced in the solution containing 10^{-5} mol dm^{-3} silver nitrate compared with the control test. Show your working.

Answer ....

(2 marks)

(ii)   Suggest an explanation for the effect of silver nitrate solution on the activity of the enzyme sucrase.

....

....

....

(2 marks)

(c)   (i) Explain why it is important to maintain constant pH when investigating enzyme activity.

....

....

(2 marks)

(iii) State three precautions, other than maintaining constant pH, which should be taken to produce reliable results in the above investigation.

1

2

3

(3 marks)

(Total 11 marks)

8. An experiment was carried out with cells of carrot tissue to determine the effect of temperature on the absorption of potassium ions.

Slices of carrot tissue were immersed in a potassium chloride solution of known concentration. The changes in concentration of potassium ions in the solution were determined at intervals for 6 hours. From these measurements, the mass of potassium ions taken in by the carrot cells was found. The experiment was carried out at 2 °C and 20 °C. The solutions were aerated continuously.

The results are shown in the graph below. Absorption of potassium ions is given in micrograms of potassium per gram of fresh mass of carrot tissue (μg^{-1}).

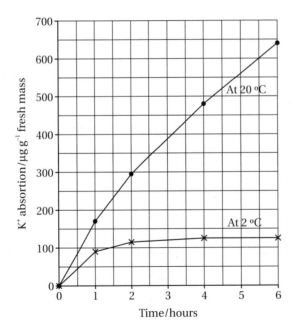

(a) During the first hour, some of the potassium ions enter the cells by diffusion. State two conditions which are necessary for a substance to enter a cell by diffusion.

1

2

(2 marks)

(b) (i) Calculate the mean rate of absorption of potassium ions at 20 °C, between 2 and 6 hours. Show your working.

Answer ....

(3 marks)

(ii) Compare the rates of absorption of potassium ions at 2 °C and 20 °C during this experiment.

....

....

....

(3 marks)

(iii) Suggest an explanation for the differences in the rates of absorption of potassium ions at the two temperatures.

....

....

....

....

(3 marks)

(Total 11 marks)

9. Give an account of the biological significance of polysaccharides.

....

....

....

....

....

....

....

....

....

....

....

....

....

....

(Total 10 marks)

Unit test answers

Each point that ends with a semicolon (;) is worth one mark. The sign / indicates alternative answers, either of which will gain you the mark. Where the '3 max' appears, this means that any 3 of the marking points will gain you the maximum 3 marks available. Half marks are never awarded. You either get a complete mark or none at all.

1 mitochondrion ; ribosomes ; chloroplast ;
centrioles / centrosome / basal body ;
nucleus   5

2 (a) (i) A = glycerol ; B = fatty acid ;   2
     (ii) hydrolysis ;   1
  (b) they are polar molecules ;
      hydrophilic / polar, heads and hydrophobic / non-polar, tails ; form a bilayer / double layer ;
      heads outside, tails inside ;   3 max

3 (a) *notice marks are for* **comparative** *points –you must say something about each term for one mark*
      prokaryotic has no nucleus / no nuclear envelope, but eukaryotic has nucleus / nuclear envelope ;
      prokaryotic is smaller than eukaryotic ; prokaryotic has smaller ribosomes than eukaryotic ; prokaryotic has no membrane-bound organelles, eukaryotic has membrane-bound organelles (or examples – mitochondria, Golgi, ER) ; example of each – e.g. bacteria are prokaryotic, animal / plant / fungal cells are eukaryotic   3 max
  (b) fibrous proteins are usually insoluble, globular are often soluble ; fibrous proteins often have structural roles, globular often have metabolic roles ; fibrous proteins molecules are long with repeating secondary structure, globular are coiled into a ball-shape and may have quaternary structure ; example of each – e.g. collagen / keratin is fibrous, insulin / haemoglobin is globular ;   3 max

4 interphase ; chromatids ; centromere ; nucleolus ;
    metaphase ; pole ;   6

5 (a) (i) four   1
     (ii) sequence of amino acids / primary structure, of a polypeptide / protein ;   1
  (b) (i) AUG ;   1
     (ii) tRNA has, an unpaired triplet of bases / anticodon ; attaches to mRNA codon ; tRNA carries a <u>specific</u> amino acid ; correct reference to formation of a peptide bond between amino acids ;   3 max

6 (a) A = deoxyribose ; B = phosphate ; C = base / adenine / thymine ; D = hydrogen bond ;   4
  (b) (i) ring drawn around one unit made up of a circle, pentagon and square ;   1
     (ii) condensation / polymerisation ;   1

7 (a) sucrase, breaks down / hydrolyses, sucrose   1
      to glucose and fructose / to monosaccharides   1
  (b) (i) working, e.g. $(23/50) \times 100$; = 46 % ;   2
     (ii) silver nitrate is an inhibitor ; affects shape of active site ; substrate can no longer bind ; 2 max

(c) (i) pH affects shape of enzyme molecule ; by affecting hydrogen bonds / ionic bonds ; affects bonding of substrate with active site   2 max
    (ii) keep temperature constant ;
       allow time for equilibration of enzyme and substrate ; same time / temperature of heating with Benedict's ; dry precipitate to constant mass ; same volume / concentration of sucrose ; same volume / concentration of sucrase ; 3 max

8 (a) membrane must be permeable to substance ;
     there must be a concentration gradient / higher outside cell than inside ; substance must be in solution / a gas / a liquid ;   2 max
  (b) (i) 640 – 295 = 345 ; divide by 4 ;
       86.25 μg g^{-1}hour^{-1} ;   3
    (ii) *notice that each mark is awarded for a <u>comparative</u> point, not just a description of one or the other*
       fastest uptake <u>for both</u> occurs at the start / rate of uptake decreases <u>for both</u> as time goes on ; rate of uptake at 20 °C is greater than at 2 °C ; rate of uptake at 20 °C continues to increase with time, whereas at 2 °C it levels off ; comparative manipulation of figures – e.g. final mass taken up is 5 × greater at 20 °C than at 2 °C   3 max
    (iii) increase in temperature increases kinetic energy / movement of potassium ions so diffusion takes place faster at 20 °C than at 2 °C ; diffusion no longer occurs when there is no concentration gradient ; but ions are also taken up by active transport which is increased at higher temperature ; because respiration takes place faster / more ATP made, at higher temperature cells may use more potassium ions (in metabolism) at higher temperature   3 max

9 polysaccharide molecules consist of many monosaccharides linked by glycosidic bonds ; detail of glycosidic bond formation including release of water molecule ; polysaccharides are insoluble ; starch is used for storage in plants and glycogen in animals ; starch is a mixture of amylose and amylopectin ; formed from α 1–4 glucose ; amylopectin / glycogen, also have 1–6 branches ; spiral shape held by hydrogen bonds forms compact shape ; no osmotic effects ; can be broken down to glucose that can be used as substrate for respiration ; cellulose is structural material in plant cell walls ; formed from β 1–4 glucose ; molecules lie straight with hydrogen bonding between neighbouring molecules ; provides high tensile strength ; glycoproteins contain polysaccharide components ; example of glycoprotein function ;   10 max